White Sands

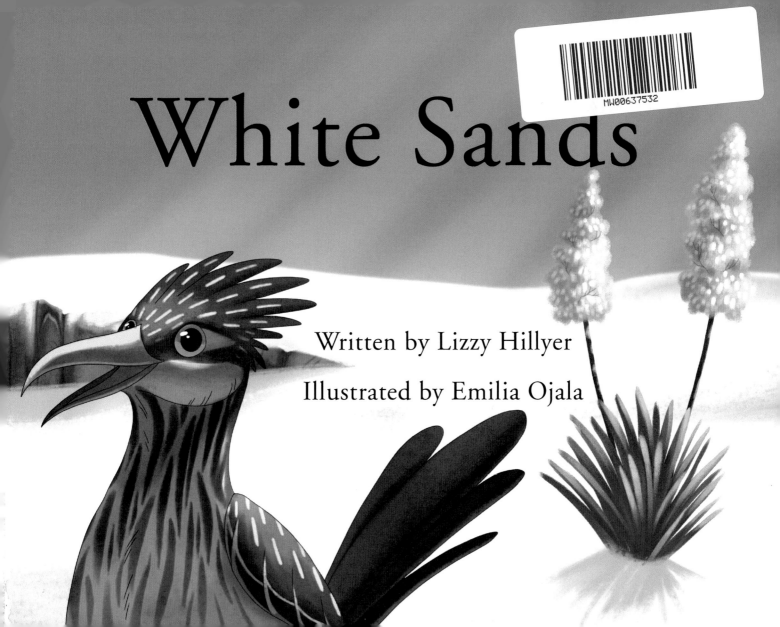

Written by Lizzy Hillyer

Illustrated by Emilia Ojala

A special thank you to my son Colton,
for being a constant source of inspiration.

"There is nothing so American as our national parks. The scenery and the wildlife are native. The fundamental idea behind the parks is native. It is, in brief, that the country belongs to the people, that it is in process of making for the enrichment of the lives of all of us." – President Franklin D. Roosevelt

In a place where sand is created by saltification,
You will find a great destination!

White as the snow, you sure won't miss 'em,
Sand dunes, made out of gypsum.

At the adobe visitor center, there's quite a stunner,
You may spot a greater roadrunner!

Great for seasoning foods, growing with a silvery tint,
Is the tasty hoary rosemary mint.

In the dunes, it's thirty feet stuck-a,
There's a beautiful Soaptree Yucca.

Little hummingbirds say, "hello,"
While they nest in the desert willow.

Out on the sand, white as a blizzard,
Can you catch a glimpse of the bleached earless lizard?

At night, past the visitor center adobe,
Roams packs of desert coyotes!

Hopping around on its back legs with a pat-pat-pat,
Hippity hoppity; The kangaroo rat.

In the desert, fuzzy like socks,
Is a playful little kit fox.

The moon is still up, but now the night shrinks.
Just in time, you spot the lynx!

More than a sandbox, the White Sands stands apart,
Because between blue skies and white sands,
is where adventures start!

About White Sands National Park

Before it was named the White Sands National Park, it was first designated as the White Sands National Monument on January 18, 1933.

It became America's 62nd National Park on December 20, 2019.

While this book shows some of the plants and animals you will find in the area, it doesn't show all of them. There are over 800 animal species alone! Amazing right?

You can learn more about the animals and the White Sands National Park at www.nps.gov/whsa.

Thank you for reading!